HOLDIN THE MIRROR

True stories about public service in a post-truth world

Curated by Dawn Reeves and Fran Collingham

HOLDING UP THE MIRROR

True stories about public service in a post-truth world

Curated by Dawn Reeves and Fran Collingham

shared press

First paperback edition published
in Great Britain in 2017 by Shared Press
Published by Shared Press
www.sharedpress.co.uk

ISBN: 978-1-9998123-0-0

Design and typesetting: Dylan Martin
www.friedbanana.co.uk

Shared Press' policy is to use papers that are natural, renewable
and recyclable products from well managed forests in accordance
with the rules of the Forest Stewardship Council.

To all the dedicated and inspiring generations
of public servants and in particular to the future
leaders who contributed to this book.

CONTENTS

FOREWORD

In these strange, post-truth times it feels harder than ever to find the space to think, question and talk to each other about what we do and why we do it. That's why organisations like Solace are, I believe, more important than ever. It's more than about support, learning from each other and sharing our triumphs and challenges. It's about having a bit of space to think.

The stories in this Solace book can play an important part in this thinking space. They're written by us – senior managers – and the people who will take on our roles in the future, many from our successful Solace Springboard programmes. Some of the stories are fictionalised and creative but very close to home (including the grim reality) and some are fascinating insights in the day to day challenges we're all facing up to in councils small and large across the country. Some are more optimistic than others – but who, working in our sector today, hasn't been struck by the contrast of some days when it feels like wading through treacle and some days when it feels like it's all to play for?

Don't ever tell me that our sector lacks creativity; innovation, risk taking, vision and purpose leap out of these pages – balanced by the pragmatic realism of the everyday grind. This is us – and these are some of the ideas that will continue to make what we do relevant and even more important over the next few years.

Uncertain times call for exceptional leaders. I've never been in any doubt that we have these across all our services in local government; the evidence is here in this book.

Do tell us your story – we'd love to hear it.

Jo Miller
President Solace

Mirrors reflect who we are - and more.

Sometimes the images can be reassuring (we're still here, gazing back at ourselves.) And if our experience shows in the mirror that's fine, too. Mirrors reveal details we might not have noticed or didn't want to see, the aspects we're not comfortable with. Our reflection stares us in the face. And a mirror can also throw rays of light on where we might be going.

It's a brave move to see ourselves through the eyes of those coming up through the ranks, aspiring leaders in the sector, those who will take over the reins in local government. Amongst some of the contributors it's possible to see aspects of our younger selves; current Solace members – chief executives, directors and senior managers - have been their role models. Yet their lenses are different, sharper, perhaps more human, closer to the frontline and the communities they serve.

This book gives us a unique insight into the working worlds of aspiring public service leaders, and people working in and with the sector, and our future direction. Their stories illustrate how they make sense of the world they work in – a world where austerity is taken for granted, the media talks about an era of post-truth and there are no longer any certainties in any area of politics.

The last decade has brought about a sea change in the public sector, how we imagine our worlds and ourselves in it. There have been positive transformations in the painful context of cuts. There are hopes and fears. Our contention is that we need to see and be open about both to fully engage with the future and then shape it.

So post-truth in this book isn't just alternative facts and fake news. The stories speak of uncomfortable realities that we don't talk enough about. They address the experience of telling truth to power (and to the people) in local government now. This isn't about appeals to emotion rather than rationality, but it does illuminate how it feels to work in a sector under threat, dogged by doom and gloom narratives and yet relied upon to deal with issues at the heart of public and private life in the UK today.

What stood out to us amongst the mirror's reflections – what the stories say to those already leading our organisations - is that you are respected teachers, widely admired. The younger generation see your bravery and resilience and love you for it. There are also challenges – about the diversity of leadership, culturally and generationally, alongside views that current leaders don't accept challenge enough, they aren't close enough to the experience of the messy lives of residents and communities they serve and there's a tendency to smooth over the bad bits. There needs to be a stronger light shone into the darker places, the too difficult box.

The collection shows in concrete and imaginative ways (we always need both) that the role of local government and public services is vital, it's a fundamental part of what makes our places tick and (with one arm tied behind its back) ensures their future. We face not only our own hopes and fears, but those of residents, businesses and communities.

As curators of the book (and former senior managers) it's been a great experience to collaborate with this group. It's given us, and we hope everyone who reads this book, a boost. It's honest, challenging and inspiring by turns. The contributors are a fantastic bunch; whatever happens in the future, the sector is in good hands.

About the book

The stories are a mix of personal narratives, opinion and fictionalised stories. Fiction enables us to make both head and heart connections. We've grouped the contributions into five themed chapters:

- Self-belief (and dogged determination)
- Authenticity (and nuance)
- Courage (and vulnerability)
- Critical thinking (and speaking-up)
- Imagination (being the future and realising change)

Many of the stories cross more than one theme. They suggest leadership qualities that many readers will be familiar with – it particularly chimes with some of the characteristics in the 21st Century Public Service work that Solace, the Local Government Association and the PPMA produced in 2016. Yet they go deeper, unearth a pithy core that illustrates what we're thinking but don't often say. This isn't a "how to" book, the stories are an invitation to engage with a different set of perspectives, close enough to recognise, yet different enough to show us something new.

Acknowledgements

Thanks to everyone who has taken the time to contribute to this project – the Solace Springboard cohorts, the chief executives who nominated colleagues and our friends, thinkers and writers who became part of the writing team, especially Chris West. We know time is precious and the process has relied on people's goodwill and ability to meet a tight deadline. Thanks to Solace and its president, Jo Miller for commissioning the book. Many thanks to our sponsor Grant Thornton. Thanks also to our designer Dylan Martin for designing a book that's striking from front to back.

Dawn Reeves and Fran Collingham
October 2017

SELF-BELIEF (AND DOGGED DETERMINATION)

"We fought hard to win, didn't take no for an answer. Did whatever it took."

Lee Tillman, Doncaster

"Hope locates itself in the premises that we don't know what will happen and the spaciousness of uncertainty is room to act."

Rebecca Solnit, writer

CHAPTER 1

We believe in ourselves individually and collectively. We are relentlessness in pursuit of outcomes; we achieve a lot with less. We thrive in the real world, uncertainty is normal, there are serious trials but there is all to play for. Don't under-estimate us. We know our value, even if the post-truth world doesn't see it. We are here for the long-term. What we do continues to influence the future.

IN MY BONES

LEE TILMAN

I'm from Doncaster, came back here after uni, it's in my bones.

I want us to aim high but we face serious challenges, low levels of educational attainment, lack of skilled opportunities and incoherent progression routes through training and into jobs. Doncaster has a proud rail engineering history and a good reputation so the chance to bid to Government for the National College for High Speed Rail to be located here was critical. It was a competition and the smart money was elsewhere but if we won, it would affect the lives of thousands of young people in the town and have a major impact on our economy. We fought hard to win, didn't take no for an answer. Did whatever it took.

At one point I found myself chasing Nick Clegg down the street, every contact mattered. We co-ordinated an approach to the then minister Vince Cable, built a strong coalition, prepared the best case possible and lobbied like crazy. The council threw in land, project managed the build and gave bursaries to local people to benefit from the college. You have to get stuck in.

Like much of our work, the outcomes were uncertain. We deal with ambiguity all the time. It's normalised but not easy. My response is to break situations down, articulate the next small steps of each part of the journey. I go through what we know and what we don't know, and go through it again. It's got to the stage now where it's liberating to take the next step. Our managers and staff want us to provide clarity when no-one has clarity. The more I share, the more everyone realises we're in it together.

One of my challenges is to listen more, to listen behind the words. We're all so busy it's easy to hear what you want to hear. I'm not the finished article but I'm proud of developing others and want to do more of that. I try to stay in the moment and not think too far in front. I like hill-walking, one foot after the other, it helps keep my focus on the now.

After three years of work, I've just seen the Eurostar Train Driver Simulator delivered to the National College for High Speed Rail. It felt amazing. If it's the right thing to do, we need to be relentless.

THE FABRIC OF THE PLACE

HELEN YORKE

Recently I had an angry man bring his four children to see me. His planning application had been refused and he demanded I explain to each of them why they couldn't have their own bedroom. I managed to get him to a place where he understood the decision even though he didn't like the result. But another day an elderly lady bought me a big bunch of flowers for helping her understand the implications of her neighbour's planning application. I'm a manager in our planning department but carry out the duty officer role; we're there to provide a service to the public whatever that brings.

Inspiring the people I manage against the backdrop of continuing austerity is hard. I'm constantly sitting down with staff, reminding them why we're here, resetting goals, checking they aren't burning out. Morale has been affected by a 2% pay cut across the board and less well paid staff are really feeling the pinch.

I try to be pro-active and focus on the important role the service plays. We are often under pressure to reduce the level of service we provide to save money. The team understand that we're not providing the gold standard anymore. There's no getting away from that; savings have to be made. Yet whatever we do is better than the scary version – where there's no service at all. None of us want that. We can't go backwards; our focus needs to be on shaping an efficient future.

There are fewer opportunities for promotion these days - so we should be investing more in training and development. I was lucky to get on a middle managers programme, it was great but I know I have more to offer. My manager and our chief executive are both really open and inspiring leaders; that's tough to do in a council with no overall control.

I'm passionate about my work and want to see local government to continue to protect and serve the public, to build a new way forward. I'm a geek, I love the built form of our environment, having an influence and improving the fabric of the place, whether that's a housing scheme or the re-development of the gardens in Dudley town centre. My work is exciting, there's no job I can't do. I'm not motivated by money; if I was, I'd work in the private sector but I know there would be a clash of values.

LEARNING TO LIVE IN OUR BI-POLAR SYSTEM

FICTION

We're in a one to one supervision meeting at a local coffee shop.

"That's absolutely brilliant." I tell Alison, our vulnerable adults manager. "The care package really works for Mrs M and I know it wasn't easy to negotiate with the family and their interpreter. The hospital bed manager messaged me her thanks. Sorry to hear about Mr B, though. Heart-breaking."

I bloody love Alison. Between the hope and despair, the life and death of it all, she finds room to manoeuvre. She even manages to laugh; a hearty infectious laugh, full of knowing and empathy. The system is mad and we are all lost in it but here we are - wherever that is.

It's the acknowledgement of the lost-ness - not cluelessness, it's never that - but being the first to say, "This is unbearable," is what makes it bearable. If we are lost together, we can find ourselves, find a way forward.

"He had a tough life, Mr B, but a good one." Alison wraps her hands tightly around her cappuccino as if she were outside. Thinking about the funeral, maybe. "His daughter was telling me about resettling here after partition, what a journey that was. It was only a few months ago they had a family do to celebrate fifty years of living in the Black Country. The grandkids loved that."

I think of my own family, our journey. We're all thinking, feeling, human beings at heart. I'm not interested in feel good stories. Or the way the media simplifies and exaggerates things. I can't be doing with lazy cynicism.

So, I'm careful about what I say. Language matters. There's a thin line between being a victim and being able to make things work. I try to acknowledge the despair but in team meetings we don't dwell on the past, the times when there was more cash around. That casts too much of a shadow for my liking, it shapes how we respond to and show up for the present.

I'm not a big fan of scenario planning either. There needs to be a bigger shift in the cosmos than reducing the number of care packages we'll need next year. Hope comes from remembering how far we've come, and charting our victories, however small.

"Mrs M, and Mr B. Let's make sure we pass both those stories on to the rest of the team."

MAKING MONEY, HAVING AN IMPACT

JONATHAN STEPHENSON

Every council has an income generation programme but not all councils have a strategy about where, how and why they want to intervene in a market. My job is about making money and having an impact, we need to be clear about what the net effect of our intervention is. I came into this role to grow and develop the local economy. There's no point in us entering successfully into a market if the result is that local businesses go to the wall.

We should only be delivering the services we are good at. And it makes sense to compete at a regional and national level, I'm not interested in being the cheapest - let others do that - we need to be building a quality brand, developing commercial skills at all levels and empowering our teams to get the best deals in the public interest. Not all council officers have a commercial sense. I try to build confidence by getting colleagues to think about their personal life - where they've negotiated a good deal, for example, on a car purchase. I gave our cemetery manager a 10% tolerance to amend prices or agree multiple purchases. Flexibility is important and if our costs go up we need to respond.

I started an events company at the age of fifteen, organising pop concerts, community gatherings and commercial launch events. I had to sell myself through the company because I was too young to have any credibility but over a three year period I gained a good reputation by providing a quality service. I'm used to working at a fast pace; the organisation can work at a much slower pace which can be frustrating.

Working within a public service framework, the moral and ethical decision-making around commerciality is key. For some people trying to hit an income target that might feel like a constraint or a frustration, but it's not for me. I totally understand that our organisational purpose is to serve the public. My dad worked in leisure and culture in a local authority. As a discretionary service, that part of the council's business is often more dynamic and entrepreneurial, it has to be.

When my dad said, "Don't work in the public sector," I suppose it provided me with a challenge. I thought I'll be the radical intervention, the one who makes it tick.

23

TRUST AND OPTIMISM

MICHELLE NUTTALL

The thing I enjoy most about this role is the stories from the frontline. At the moment we're providing our social care staff with new technology to help them engage differently with people. One story was of an elderly man who wasn't thought capable of making decisions for himself. But the technology enabled a different conversation – it turned out he was profoundly deaf, and couldn't see the small font on paper forms. Expanding text on the tablet showed he did understand, and allowed him to participate in his own care. A small example of how we need to challenge our assumptions. Our focus needs to be on how we deepen our understanding of what works. Trusting our staff – and learning from them – is vital.

It doesn't have to be delivered by us either; we need to trust other organisations. I see more recognition that a joint approach to doing what's best for the individual is right – that's also how we'll hit all of our savings targets.

Our job in local government is to be ambitious for our places – if we don't do it, no-one else will. Working with others, which includes working at a regional level on some issues, raises questions around the sovereignty and autonomy of our organisation and that can be uncomfortable. We have to think flexibly. We can't defend existing structures if the outcomes for people are still poor.

To make this agenda happen we need to attract, invest in and retain more young talent. Millennials are said to choose their jobs based on values; why aren't there more of them working in local government? The way we're seen externally doesn't reflect the reality of my experience; we're encouraged to innovate and take risks to make a difference to Kirklees.

I'd like to see us enabling more career movement across sectors, we need to get into the too difficult box, tackle some of the big obstacles behind the scenes like terms and conditions. I think about my career in three year chunks not decades. I'll be spreading my wings at some point, looking for a wider role.

A COALITION OF THE WILLING

ROB GREGORY

I worry that our organisations don't see that the world is changing. As individuals, of course we know the way people live their lives isn't neat and tidy, it's complicated and messy. We say we get it. And yet too often we carry on thinking and providing services in more or less the same way that we've always done.

We look at a family and describe them as "service users." They don't see themselves as a "LAC family." School holidays are a classic, they can be highly stressful times for vulnerable families, they need support, activities and access to services but many of these services just don't have the capacity. Not directly because of cuts but because many of their staff work on term-time contracts. It takes time to collectively unpick and work through the organisational boundaries to understand what matters to the people we are supposed to be helping.

A target driven culture remains that sees cases processed and referred when we actually know that what people often want is time and a better appreciation of what they need to move forward.

26

In Great Yarmouth our approach to early help and early intervention was informed by a community development ethos. We took county council colleagues on this journey to appreciate the assets within communities and to add value in neighbourhoods, challenging staff to think outside their core offer and to work with people on a range of different issues. It wasn't formulaic, it was organic - but that was also its strength.

We need to reflect more. Spend more time thinking about the way people live, the sorts of skills they have and might need. It's an uncomfortable space for many leaders in local government. Is there really a common ownership of how things are in our places?

I've tried hard to embed a can-do culture. I give staff autonomy to make decisions. They aren't doing the same things every day, the roles are developmental. They like the fact they can challenge how things are and can influence what happens in their town. That's the same thing that motivates me.

27

AUTHENTICITY (AND NUANCE)

"It's about surfacing alternative versions of the truth, applying context and improving understanding."

Kate Waterhouse, Manchester

"Not everything that is faced can be changed, but nothing can be changed until it is faced."

James Baldwin, writer and critic

CHAPTER 2

We are open – not selectively – authentic. We acknowledge what's difficult about our world, like navigating political and people power, the wider threats and financial challenges. We don't defend the indefensible, don't pretend. We demonstrate our authenticity by being both thinking and feeling – not dragged into fear-driven emotional reactions. We provide meaningful intelligence and help to make sense of complexity through the stories we tell. We don't indulge in conspiracy theories, we show, don't tell. Our future role is about articulating where there is consensus and the potential for it. Our choices, about our leadership practice and our careers, are always nuanced.

SPEAKING TRUTH TO POWER

CAT ORCHARD

Speaking truth to power - exactly how important it is and how best to go about doing it - has become a hot debate in this post-truth world. Most people seem to agree it's part of an officer's role, but how best to go about it has highlighted the ongoing discussion around member-officer relationships and the grey area around where the line is drawn.

Having witnessed the sudden departure of one chief executive followed, around six months later, by the sudden departure of one leader, with the whole member-officer relationship issue playing a sizeable part in both, the consequences of speaking truth to power seem, right now, to mean that someone's head ends up on a plate in a relatively dramatic fashion.

Young (ish) as I am, I am not naive enough to assume that we should all just get along nicely all the time. Disagreement is healthy. Debate is healthy. Discussion is healthy. Heaven knows, we do enough of it amongst ourselves as officers, and our political colleagues do the same. I also understand and appreciate that officers are employed, while our member colleagues have an electoral mandate that they need to deliver on. That places us at different starting points.

But I don't think it's right that, as officers, we should view our role as delivering a political mandate (unless it's illegal) or to front up the difficult news, with our political colleagues having the monopoly on positivity and hope. I think that's too binary a view of the local government world and it does a disservice to those authorities where members and officers work together successfully as a team and deliver amazing things for their communities. It's also a really unhelpful view for an authority where the member-officer culture isn't functioning as well. In our current austerity-driven world, where so much relies on staff going that extra mile, chief executives need to be able to bring their organisation with them, and drive a vision for the organisation, much in the same way that elected members need the support of the public to deliver their vision. The skills sets are not dissimilar.

Ultimately both sides of the local government coin do what they do to improve the lives of the communities around them, both sides are responsible for both the positive and negative impacts of decisions and both sides should be able to discuss with each other how they go about doing that in a respectful way.

SHOPPING WITH MUM

FICTION

"What do you think? Shall we buy it?" The finance director looks like Jade's mum, smart, affordable dresses in bold greens and blues, easy to iron.

"Hmmm…" Jade forces her shoulders to relax, she knows they are only making recommendations but, still.

It is a Mercedes garage on the south coast with 12 acres of land, housing is a possibility.

In front of them is a list of properties for sale, including sites in parts of the country she's never heard of.

"What about the office block, badly converted to flats but in a desirable location? It's much cheaper," she fiddles with a metal hair-grip, trying to keep her hair neat.

"But will the yields hold up long-term?" the boss asks. "Buy cheap and we might regret it."

Ugh, that reminds Jade of interminable shopping trips with her mother looking at every label, going on about the quality of the fabric. Not a clue about fashion. Jade feels a lecture coming on.

"Secure the bricks and mortar." The director repeats the mantra. "Every pound we generate is a cut we don't have to make."

"But…" Jade doesn't want to sound negative, "There's been another article in the FT," the alarm bells are sounding louder, "Is local government borrowing the next financial bubble ready to burst?"

"You're a bright young woman; you can work out what's opinion and what's fact. Who's writing those stories and why."

Truth is, this whole buying property thing is keeping Jade awake at night, that and her own newly acquired mortgage, her un-dented student debt. It's not the first time she's wondered about looking for another job, working somewhere more risk averse.

"I know but is it the right thing to be doing?" Jade asks.

"The right thing is to deliver better outcomes for our residents," the director says sternly, "And needs must."

That's straight out of her mum's book. Her mum had to be careful with money but she'd made sure that Jade, and her sister Jas, had everything they needed.

"Let's go and visit the Mercedes garage and the flats, have a poke around."

Another sleepless night, radio voices used to help her settle. The whispered news talks of personal debt on the rise, the UK owes 31 trillion pounds, the US owes ten times that. Buying the site is nothing in comparison to the mountains of debt. But what does that say to potential inward investors? There's no point in investing here, no income to be made. Jade feels the world tilt on its axis, cracks appear.

33

X MARKS THE SPOT

PALBINDER SANDHU

I was working on the day of the EU referendum as a presiding officer in a polling station with a team of three poll clerks. It was our usual station, a school canteen, and my fifth time there.

We noticed a lot of first time voters entering nervously, unlike previous years where we saw the same familiar faces.

"I've never done this before so you'll have to tell me what to do," a lady in her 30s said as she pushed her daughter's pram.

As the day went on we noticed the number of people questioning the use of the pencils that were neatly sharpened and tied with string to the side of every ballot booth. We realised the conspiracy theorists were not isolated to our location when a text message was received mid-morning from the elections unit, confirming it was okay for people to use pens, as long as their vote was clearly marked.

"I need a pen! I know they'll rub it out and change it - I'm not stupid y'know!" said one forthright man, storming off to cast his vote after I passed him a biro to use.

"Can I just ask, why do you always give us pencils?" asked one woman, after she had cast

---

her vote - with a pen. "It's just what we traditionally use but you can always use a pen," I replied.

"Well, it's ridiculous and it's because of things like this we need to leave the EU!" she sternly said as she left. Only nine more hours to go.

As #usepens gained momentum on social media, we saw many voters who were only happy to vote using a pen. I even saw voters sneaking their own pens out of their pockets and bags; one woman pulled a pen from her high bun hairdo and snuck it back in afterwards.

I spoke to a regular voter who wanted to use a pen. I explained to him the process of securing the ballot box after the vote at 10pm and taking it to the count where the votes would be counted straight away, assuring him it was all done under surveillance.

"Everyone on Facebook is saying vote with a pen, so I'm using my pen," he replied.

So many people had been swept up in the frenzy over Brexit - and the fact was it had meant a greater turnout. Maybe in future we could save money by asking voters to bring their own pens!

STILL PART OF THE UNION

FICTION

We're like one big family here. The PR people like that – they think it makes us sound like something out of The Waltons. Actually, I think we're more like one of those families on the Jeremy Kyle show – all shouting at each other, lying to each other, stabbing each other in the back when things go wrong.

But it's true that lots of us – the real workers, I call them, not the management imports who are here for a couple of years before they move on and up – are someone's sister, cousin, father, husband. We used to be the biggest employer here and anyone who wanted a job security and a bit of a pension at the end of the day knew it was the place to work. We always looked after each other and there was a bit of pride (not that we'd tell our mates in the pub this, of course) in delivering services that mattered to our neighbours.

The bosses have been making cuts and shaving bits off here and there for years and we've been getting by, but it's miserable stuff and no-one's happy about it. My lads in the depot are on at me all the time to get it sorted. Now we've reached the crunch point. The leader says the only way to balance the books is to make big cuts in big services. Our biggest cost is our people, he says, and that's what we've got to tackle. People who are my members. My friends and relatives. Out of a job – a job they thought they'd have for life.

We went to school together, me and the leader. Known each other for decades. Even stood on a picket line together when we were young firebrands. Now he's got a choice – back the unions, who gave him his start in life, who he sees at party meetings all the time, who are looking after his voters – or take us on and see the bin bags pile up in the streets.

So I'm going to knock on the door of his fancy giant office in the Town Hall, sit myself down at his important conference table and spell it out to him. I feel sorry for him, really. But that's politics, and that's how it has to be done these days.

37

LET'S GIVE IT A GO

CLARE STOREY

The employee from the council tax team was anxious. She didn't want to move to the new customer services centre. All that open space, no protective screens shielding her from people. Like many of her colleagues she was worried about working in a new way – and she made it clear to me that she didn't think we'd made the right call.

But by noon on the first day the new centre was open she searched me out, found me and told me that now she'd done it and was working in a new way she thought it was the best thing ever.

It's those moments that keep me going and help me stay optimistic and focused on the next challenge in the constantly changing environment I work in.

I'm managing and leading a team of committed, enthusiastic people after arriving here as a graduate trainee a decade ago. We work really hard to convince the rest of the organisation that change can be a good thing.

I don't have an alternative way – that helps. Older, cynical people say, we've tried this before, it won't work. We're a young team who hasn't tried it before and so we try to think creatively about how we could sort it - and watch each other's backs.

I wish we didn't need my job. There shouldn't be a transformation programme, really. Change should just be part of everyone's day job and business as usual for us all.

I didn't realise at first that my approach to leadership isn't the same as others. Talking to people in an open way, being accessible in an open plan office. Actually, that's not always how everyone operates and that can make things difficult.

I'm passionate about public service. I want to deliver change for the better for the council and the people we serve…but it's tough. I'm not sure about being a senior manager.

I look at the senior managers I know and it's all consuming for them. Work life balance is important to me. I want to use my skills to make a difference, but I may not be able to do that in local government.

THE TRUSTED MESSENGER: HOLD FIRE! THIS ISN'T THE END OF THE EXPERT.

KATE WATERHOUSE

In this confusing world of fake news and dodgy data your research community might have their heads in hands - in fear of the future and their jobs. For every data source that exists, there is another that seeks to discredit it. There's a danger that analysts just become part of an echo chamber for decision makers, providing slick visualisations and eye-catching info-graphics that act as a cloak of legitimacy.

My contention, however, is that whilst people may be more sceptical about data this doesn't mean they don't want it, they just want – and deserve – better data. What people need is a trusted guide to provide meaningful insight. We need to be the trusted messenger.

Without such guides, my sense is that people are building their own personal versions of the truth, often from the ground up, using data sources that they have created, whether this is lifestyle data through wearable technology or individual weather recordings to monitor the seasons. Feeling close to the source of the data is important, as is being able to set the rules of engagement so that data is not intrusive but insightful. We must learn from that; personalisation may be the key to acceptance.

Personalisation means researchers getting better at providing information residents and colleagues recognise, perhaps because they were part of creating it, or can see themselves within it. It must be presented in a way that makes sense and gives people confidence to use it. This shows empathy and helps validate their view of the world, helping to tackle the feelings of insecurity that could characterise a post-truth world.

Yet we must also stay true to our purpose of challenging views that are not supported by objective information and hold people to account; otherwise the prophecy will come true and researchers will become dispensable.

There will always be different versions of the truth as there will always be parallel realities based on personal experiences and histories. Better data is about surfacing these alternative versions, applying context and improving understanding. This is what we researchers do best.

Achieving this allows collaboration between the holders of those different views, facilitating better decision making and stronger planning. It's how we achieve outcome based decision making in a post-truth world. The death of local government research and intelligence function is, as they say, greatly exaggerated.

41

THEM AND US

FICTION

Paul watches the council leader's fat grey tongue sweep the biscuit crumbs from his top lip.

"This scheme will bring £6.6million in new investment to the town, 120 new jobs and by building the capacity of the community, it will lead to 250 grand's worth of savings," Paul repeats the facts.

"Jobs for them. Not us. That's what I've heard." A slurp echoes in the councillor's faded silver jubilee mug.

Paul slows his breathing, maintains eye contact. They've been round this loop roughly every three months since the new councillors were elected.

"The business plan has been produced independently and verified by the Arts Council, Heritage England and the Bank. We've set up a community interest company with representatives from all sections of the community."

"Their communities, not ours."
Don't rise to it, Paul tells himself, the final approval, that's all he needs.

"Your deputy – who's a director of the new company - said it was okay."

"He says we're putting in thousands and we won't see a penny of the cash."

"The town benefits from every penny. The community interest company will administer the grants. The council contribution is £48,000 – 7% of the £6.6million."

"That means we're right. A bloke in the pub said…" Paul looks at the sneer on the leader's face and puts his folder of evidence away.

"So we'll be voting against it. End of."

Two years of hard work and a real opportunity to change the place dismissed in a beat.

"I don't get it," Paul can't stop himself. "Why wouldn't you want this?"

"Look you're not a bad lad… but you'll never be one of us." The leader takes the biscuits and heads off.

*

At home Paul reads the story in the evening paper.

"Council wastes two years on dumped scheme, tax payers' money squandered on consultants. Council leader calls for vote of no confidence in senior management."

He stares at the headline. As he downs a glass of red wine, he thinks back to the leader's election campaign.

This man got in on a ticket of sorting out the corrupt useless council. The new leader had found nothing of the sort.

This isn't about sabotaging the investment scheme because it's not for them, Paul realises. The leader's need to be right is greater than his desire to improve the place. They thrive on failure. If the town improves they are wrong.

45

COURAGE (AND VULNERABILITY)

"Those who do nothing, do nothing wrong."

Stephen Gaskell, quoting Southwark CEX Eleanor Kelly

"I define vulnerability as uncertainty, risk and emotional exposure. There is a myth that vulnerability is weakness. Vulnerability is the birthplace of love, belonging, joy, courage and creativity. It is the source of hope, empathy, accountability and authenticity. Vulnerability is not knowing victory or defeat, it's understanding the necessity of both; it's engaging. It's being all in."

Brene Brown, writer and academic.

CHAPTER 3

In the face of momentous events we step up, we often have a unique and unseen role. People might question how relevant local government is; "They ought to do something…" We are the "they" that people rely on in crises. We feel the fear and take action. We have the courage to be human, to reach out to communities that aren't like us, don't think like us, to break out of our echo chambers. We don't accept the way the world is framed. Things can be different.

LONDON BRIDGE IS CLOSED

STEPHEN GASKELL

"London Bridge is closed."

Rumours spread like a virus through the queue leaving the Depeche Mode gig at the Olympic Stadium, six miles away. My partner said, "I know what you're thinking but we have to get home first. Then make the calls."

The system worked well, our emergency planning manager already had the response centre set up. I tried to get my head down for a couple of hours until I was due to take over at Silver Control but my subconscious was turning it all over.

The big issues at Silver Control were the need for the clean-up to be dignified and respectful of the continuing police investigation, the cordon around the station and the effect on the residents, the cathedral and businesses inside it and the planning for Monday morning; would the station open? At its peak thousands of people are passing through at any one time.

We planned for all scenarios - fully open, partial or not at all. We couldn't assume anything, nor predict which way it would go.

"I need a message," our comms manager said.
"We don't have one," I replied calmly.
"I can't say we don't know."
"But we don't know."

It was important to hold our nerve. When the message came from Gold Control that there was to be a limited opening, we were prepared and the message was right first time. Our chief executive says, "Those who do nothing wrong, do nothing." I'll always remember that.

Throughout the emergency, I was constantly worried about forgetting something, the impact on other work and battling with focus over fatigue. Then, before we knew it, the General Election was on and I was part of team leading it. And then our chief executive was pulled into the Grenfell response. The whole organisation was like an elastic band stretched to its max in the face of some of London's toughest days and weeks.

It's hard to know when to step back, to recognise when it's time to let go. The Chief Fire Officer for London said recently, "It's okay not to be okay," and that she was receiving counselling. It's important to be true to yourself. I build my resilience through a powerful support network. You can be a super-technocrat and get the job done, but the relationships, at all levels, are what make the real difference.

49

WHAT I'M REALLY THINKING

THE COUNCILLOR

I want to get this right, to chair this committee the same as I would any other. But I'm bound to say the wrong thing. I should've paid more attention in the training.

I fear for the trans community. The murder last year was scary.

THE TRANS-COMMUNITY REP

Me, in a Council Chamber! I can hear your voice slowing down. You're trying hard not to stare and I appreciate that but trust me, I'm more nervous than you.

You don't know what a relief it is to live here, to have a community. When my brother beat me up for about the 100th time, I borrowed money from my mum's purse, took my rucksack and came here. I tried to pay her back but she wouldn't take it. This city is a safe haven.

THE COUNCILLOR

But I'm also worried this is going to cost us money we haven't got. I want to respect everyone's human rights, but we can't respond to every minority group, the list is endless.

We're bound to be vilified in the Daily Mail.

The last time something like this came up the committee chair got hate mail. To be fair, the group have got their heads around the LGB – but the T is far more challenging.

THE TRANS–COMMUNITY REP

What I really want probably sounds trivial to you. I used to swim for my school but I can't handle the changing rooms now, people judging my body. Surely we could get an hour on the timetable just for us.

You're thinking it's all about the toilets. But seriously what's the problem with changing the signs to unisex? I couldn't book a GP appointment because my form got rejected, I'm not Mr, Ms or Mrs. You don't know what it's like, they didn't believe it was me. And I have to go to London for my hospital appointments, it costs a fortune.

51

WHAT I'M REALLY THINKING

THE COUNCILLOR

Bring it on, is what I say. That's why I'm a Councillor, to stand up for people, for a fairer society. The more prejudice I see, the more I'm determined to do what we can.

Preparing for this meeting has made me realise how much in life is set up for me. I'm humbled that you've taken the time to come today.

THE TRANS-COMMUNITY REP

I'm glad to be here though. Whatever happens next, we've been given a chance to be heard. It's a first. An opportunity I'll never forget.

RE-ESTABLISHING
THE CONNECTION

FICTION

"Never ask a question if you don't want the answer."

That was our team's mantra when I was an up and coming policy officer, exploring a brave new world of consultation and engagement. We had the lot in those days – surveys, focus groups, workshops... we'd ask people about anything and everything. We even had an internal workshop so staff could decide where the loos should go in a new community building. There was money around and we were determined to spend it with the widest possible buy-in.

It feels like a long time ago – it was, I suppose. It seems laughable, now, that we took so much time and did so much thinking about things. I don't even have a policy team to tell this story to now.

Well. Last June we asked a question and the public gave us the answer many of us didn't want. The disconnect was shocking. After the austerity cuts, losing our EU funding felt like the final nail in the coffin for the local government.

And yet the message from Lands End is that we're still here. There's still a need for us; not just to empty bins and look after vulnerable children but to shape the places we live in and make them better for the next generation. Our intentions were right and proper but the way I see it now, our survival - the success of our communities and our organisations, depends on us listening and learning – communities, staff and politicians. So I won't be asking survey questions about housing needs. I'll try to understand why each person here is homeless or in trouble. I'll break out of my echo-chamber, hear the things I might've closed my ears to in the past.

That will be harder. But there's no-one else to do the connecting, to solder the wires. I like the idea of soldering, there's heat, sparks and energy. Our backs might be against the wall but we come out fighting. We crack on, forge a new way forward. Bolder, braver and more fearless. We start saying yes again.

A CONVERSATION WITH MYSELF...

KATIE HALE

Roll up, roll up, we have jugglers, plate spinners and magicians galore, Sounds familiar I think... what will today have in store?

Five meetings, ninety nine emails, a policy to update, it's okay.

Communicate, collaborate, negotiate, I must relate and not be late.
It's okay. I am here until eight.

Change is not new but the challenges are,
We must know our own values and fine tune our radar.

Courage and truth, aspirational traits,
But in a new post truth world, is it all too late?

We do more with less, we are agile. Maybe we are fragile.
Are we running on empty or do we still have plenty?

Wait, hold on, what am I thinking?
We are not sinking, neither is our commitment shrinking.

Our communities, our purpose it is our duty to excel, our teams are strong, no time to dwell.

Embracing change, helping others too,
Be bold and clear, public sector to the rescue.

Grit and determination, compassion and care,
Our future is out there, ready to share.

A chance to influence, to flourish, to thrive, stand strong and build futures as we rise and revive.

We may be jugglers, plate spinners and more but the future is out there, come let us explore.

BRINGING MYSELF TO WORK

RACHEL JONES

Actually I like to bring my better self to work. I'm always positive and optimistic. I don't tell people I work in HR (I head up a fully traded HR service that supports schools) I say, I run a small business. We deliver what matters to our customers.

I was encouraged from a very early age to try new things. My mum's family were Italian immigrants so to avoid being an outsider we got stuck in, whatever it was. At work, whether it's being the first to implement a new digital solution for appraisals, developing an innovative council-wide approach to service redesign or making a video instead of a report on a leadership programme, I like to take risks and bring things to life.

I watch my kids and think, so why did they do that? They ask why all the time, I do that too. It's refreshing. My eldest (aged eight) really learns through IT. Councils have to move fast so that when she grows up we're not lumbering behind with systems and bureaucracy that get in the way or hold us back. My resilience comes from the experience of taking new things on (for better or worse) and learning from it.

The single most important thing I've done was to take a very well-known and experienced senior teacher through the process of prohibition from teaching. It was the first case in the country, the pressure was immense. Although there were no allegations of abuse, we'd been made aware of patterns of behaviour that seemed wrong. For me there was no choice but to act.

I wasn't prepared for the backlash though. I became a target. There were countless testimonials supporting the teacher, including MPs and magistrates, and complaints about me. There were some deep, difficult moments but I worked solidly with the head teacher, the National College for Teaching and Leadership and the Department for Education. In the public hearing though, I stood alone. It was a relief when the order came through.

The experience gave me perspective and what doesn't kill you… as they say. I love my work.

I get a great sense of achievement from knowing that I support children to get the best education they can, I support the council corporately and make sure my small business thrives.

CONFIDENT IN SCARY SPACES

OLIVER MORLEY

I'll start with a lady, let's call her Karen, she's in her 50s and works in a warehouse. A housing association tenant, coming to terms with her kids recently leaving home, she's doing okay.

Then there's a minor accident with a trolley, her leg is injured and she can't do her job, depression follows. As the bedroom tax kicks in, she's threatened with eviction. In three months all her stability has gone and she's facing the prospect of a life dependent on the state, away from her family home.

There are many Karens and these are the cases I take home with me. Simple issues, terrible outcomes. I speak to friends in the NHS, housing, education and police and the overlap between organisations is massive. Our challenge is to fundamentally change the system for people like Karen.

I was responsible for a major transformation project tackling welfare reforms. Using data and insight we targeted the 700 people who were going to lose more than £50 a month, some over £300. It was bloody hard work, people were emotional and angry. Our challenge was to tell it absolutely

---

straight, to let people know what they were dealing with. There were no easy choices.

In return, they were open with us and we were able to put the right support in place to make it work. We were feeling our way, creating new pathways and a lot of what we did flew in the face of traditional ways of local government working. The gratitude we received was humbling and there were savings for the public purse long-term – 400 people found work.

This type of work is personal for me. I was born in 1979, grew up in the north east in the 80s. When I was seven I accidently smashed a window at school playing football.

My teacher, Mrs Wilde, sat me down and explained the consequences. If she kept having to fix windows, there were a whole list of other things she couldn't afford. I learnt early about living through tough times.

What scares me is that if we don't change ourselves we have solutions forced on to us from outside. I'm using similar approaches in my new job, focusing on different population groups, people with dementia, those at risk of falls and those with mental health illnesses. We have to be pro-active and prevent costly outcomes, for individuals and for our organisations.

61

CRITICAL THINKING (AND SPEAKING UP)

"The ability of a market place that is struggling to meet the needs of some of our most complex young people presents a major challenge."

Samantha Murray, St Helen's

"Critical thinking without hope is cynicism, but hope without critical thinking is naivete."

Maria Popova, writer

CHAPTER 4

We think critically on both sides of any argument – what we naturally might agree with and what we don't. We see the darker edges of our world and speak out about them: the unintended consequences of decision-making, our principles being challenged at every turn, the fragility of what we do and the unresolvable conflicts. We don't live in a neutral world and we must not be pushed over. We are rightly concerned for the future and we don't shoot the messenger. Post-truth isn't just about alternative truths, it's also about what we're not saying.

JACK'S STORY

SAMANTHA MURRAY

Jack was 14 years old when we received notice that he had to leave his current placement immediately – another placement breakdown. Jack's social worker had recently left the authority and his new social worker was only just building a relationship with him - he had already damaged her car in a recent incident.

Jack had a history of physical assaults on staff, but this last assault was the final straw. We started the search for a new provider but, despite a network of national providers, 160 refused to take the referral either because of their capacity or because they could not meet Jack's needs. Despite funding a placement at a cost of £4,000 a week, this child was 'unplaceable'. How can the market not respond? How can a network of 160 providers, charging the public purse thousands of pounds a week not meet the needs of this child?

Eventually one provider agreed to accommodate Jack at a cost of £7,000 a week. The placement lasted two weeks. Jack is now in court ordered secure accommodation. It was the right decision at that time for his safety and that of others. But Jack will shortly be released from secure accommodation – to where?

I have recently moved into my current post as an assistant director for children's social care following a career in housing, using my experience to help review and manage the services we provide to looked after children and a budget that is projecting to be significantly overspent. As a non-social worker this has been a huge learning curve for me. I've been struck not only by the high costs of residential placement, which can range from £2,000 to £5,000 a week, but also the rate at which these costs have increased over recent years.

The ability of a market place that is struggling to meet the needs of some of our most complex young people presents a major challenge. The impact on the child, the team around the child and the public purse is stark. We've recently taken Jack's five siblings into our care - despite many attempts at early intervention and support to parents.

How can we continue to invest in and promote effective prevention and early intervention whilst the day to day challenges like Jack's story continue? This one of the biggest challenges for national and local government and in how we make a positive and sustainable impact on the lives of our most vulnerable children.

TALKING 'BOUT
THE NEXT GENERATION

FICTION

I've worked in local government for 12 years now. I started when it was pretty much a holy grail and still regarded as the good times. You got a gratifying pension, there was flexi-time and while it was still - even then - a poor relation to the private sector for rates of pay, there was an element of job security that made you think it was definitely a good career choice.

Fast forward to aged 41 and the public sector's a very different place. Public sector pay has been frozen or at just 1% and pensions, while still favourable, are unlikely to stay that way by the time I retire.

I've been through eight restructures and in relative terms I've got off lightly. While it looks likely that public sector pay will increase, I'm pleased for myself on the one hand, but groan inwardly on the other, as I know it means that more savings will have to be found to cover the pay rise.

I joined in the heyday, the good times. When the public sector was well regarded and it felt like a job of choice. It feels a different story now; surveys nationally regularly repeat that public sector employee stress levels are sky high, we're told to do 'more with less', be more efficient, more commercial and keep on giving as you see colleagues repeatedly walk away with no-one to pick up their work.

Don't get me wrong, I'm a great believer in leaving a job if you're not happy and I am, like so many of our co-workers, resilient to the core. I also work in the public sector because I made a choice to make a difference to people's lives. But what of the next generation?

Who will be attracted to come and work in a struggling public sector where personal development and training is bottom of the pile? And where verbal abuse is on the rise or where an annual restructure is the norm? How can and will we compete to recruit the best?

Will we, like our central government funding, just wither on the vine?

67

MISSION ACCOMPLISHED

JASON O'BRIEN

Welcome agent. Please sit down. In order to ensure appropriate use of public funds I have allocated 11 minutes for your appraisal, four minutes fewer than last year.

Your figures across the board have been exemplary. Outcomes for children have been met without exception. Your reunification figures speak for themselves. Comments?

Only that none of the cases were real. I was able to establish that most of the so called unaccompanied minors were in fact accompanied - by transport agents. Paid for in advance with no legitimate claim. Asylum pleas with no substantive evidence also featured highly.

Talk me through the PK case.

Interesting due to the so called physical evidence. Mother and child showed scars in the wrist and ankle area which was said to be evidence of incarceration. Of so called torture.

Their country of origin produces jewellery. Bangles worn about the arms and legs. It was my hypothesis that these that were responsible for the scars. Severe chaffing that may have become infected. Evidence suggested that this was likely.

Evidence?

Two such wooden pieces were noticed during a visit to the facility. Mother was also seen to be scratching her wrist, supporting the theory that she had an allergy to the materials used. The warden confirmed that she wore the pieces every day. He referred to seeing her in some kind of "tribal get up".

And the child?

There was a note in the child's medical which referred to a skin rash. Hypersensitivity.

Seen together, it was clear that the only torture going on here was the type best fixed by mild antiseptic cream. This was provided to prevent future irritation.

One would think banning the bangles would be a more appropriate course of action.

Apparently it's a cultural thing, sir.

Quite. The family were reunified in June I understand?

Correct, sir. Funds earned in the Family Work Salvation Scheme covered the cost of their passage back. I understand there has been no news since their return.

No news is good news. And substantial budget savings are a key performance indicator. Your 2% salary increase is approved. Excellent social work agent, you are a credit to the profession.

SHADOWS WHEREVER WE STAND

REBECCA SMITH

The hedge separating the two front gardens is massive. It casts skyscraper shadows and a yellow laminated sign flutters on the breeze about halfway up the colossal privet as a man starts to assemble his chainsaw.

Eva stands on her porch lighting a crafty cigarette. She spies her neighbour doing the same thing.

EVA
Smiling sheepishly
Terrible habit. I'm giving Stoptober a go again this year. You fancy signing up with me? Can act as my coach. Har har!

LIZ
Mutters incoherently and continues puffing silently

EVA
I said, fancy joining me in doing Stoptober?

LIZ
Takes a long angry drag, looking at the hedge, and spits out
No. I don't want to do Stoptober, Eva. I like smoking. I like the taste and also I like the fact that I can hide behind the hedge to do so.

EVA
Confused and smile faltering
Oh. Yes, well. I guess it is very relaxing and … wait what?
The hedge's what?

LIZ
*Slowly turns and fixes a stern gaze on Eva enunciating
slowly*
The. Hedge. Is. Fine. As. It. Is.

EVA
Understanding dawning
Well. Um…yes I know it's a bit of a local fixture, but to
be honest it makes the house dark and people always
comment on how inconvenient it must be taking up most of
the garden.

LIZ
Hands on hips and cigarette on lips wagging precariously
So your solution is just 'cut it down?' No discussion, no
compromise? Just chop, chop away.
Makes wild chopping motion.

EVA
Arms spread in appeal
We did talk about it ages ago and you and Andy said
nothing. Not a word. The cost of maintenance goes up.

---

every year. It's unmanageable! Steve and Andy tried pruning it in June, remember? Nearly ended in a severed artery and Steve's thumb has never been right since.

LIZ
The hedge has always been here. People use it as a local landmark.

EVA
mutters darkly
Or as a place to hide things

LIZ
Drops cigarette and stubs it out furiously
Well, I will be lodging a complaint against your stupid pruning order. I like the shade and don't see why we have to change things to please you.

EVA
IT'S NOT JUST ME! The postman is fed up with using a machete to deliver the post, my mother's wheelchair ran aground on the roots and I've lost count of the number of cats that have gone missing in it. Why didn't you say anything before?

LIZ
Whispers menacingly
I didn't think I needed to.

EVA

Leans over and hisses
I'm not a mind reader and at this point, quite frankly, I
don't give a fu...

The shattering, ear piercing scream of a chainsaw
starting up drowns out whatever Eva continues to shout
silently at the sky.

TACKLING LITTER...
AND LONELINESS

PALBINDER SANDHU

I stand on the pavement, looking up Victor Street, in awe of the passion and commitment of over 30 volunteers made up of residents, business owners and me, the ward officer, on a hazy, sunny Sunday morning in August. This is the third community clean up in three months.

With bags of rubbish neatly piled up outside the local community centre, we all head in to celebrate another successful operation with pizza and soft drinks donated from local takeaways and shops showing their gratitude and, possibly, guilt following the initial complaints residents had made about the streets being blighted by litter.

Tensions had grown in the area and two local women, Saima and Zenub, had taken it upon themselves to take action, calling on their local councillor, who had put them in contact with me. Zenub said, "We all take pride in our homes, making them spick and span, yet we step outside and the streets are strewn with litter - where's the pride there, why don't people care?"

It's great to harness support, yet the balance is delicate in keeping volunteers motivated. People used to say, "But what do we pay our taxes for?" But over the past few years there has been understanding from most people that front line services are being reduced. So, when the group were asking people to volunteer, they were explaining that if they supported the council by volunteering, the council would provide equipment and take away the collected rubbish.

Volunteers were getting this project off the ground so the leadership of it was theirs. By organising their own clean up the community avoided bureaucracy and red tape. I explained to the group how to carry out a clean-up and supported them but they took the lead, door knocked and motivated residents to get involved by speaking in plain English and plain Urdu, Punjabi and more.

Hearing the chatter between residents of all ages and backgrounds as they enjoy the fruits of their labour, it's evident that these volunteers had not only helped clean the streets, but had also brought the community together.

However, I have a nagging feeling that all this has been developed on thin ice. What about neighbourhoods where there are no willing volunteers? Does the pro-activeness of this community mean the redeployment of council resources to other, more needy, areas? Do neighbourhoods like this one gain or lose out?

For now, all I know is there's a real feeling of community in this neighbourhood. Long may it continue.

I BELONGED TO THE BLANK GENERATION... BUT I'M ALRIGHT NOW?

FICTION

I grew up in a Midlands industrial town. I was 15 in 1977, and watched the city's fortunes collapse, as manufacturing industry melted away, accompanied by the raucous sound of new wave music telling me I belonged to the blank generation. It felt like it. I was rescued from the dole queue by escape to university, in those days an unusual course for action for someone like me.

For me, the key story of 2017 is not Brexit, or Trump or the General Election. It turns out that average incomes in pensioner households have for the first time overtaken those in working households as cohorts of pensioners who have worked, owned their own homes and have had access to good pensions (like the Local Government Pension Scheme) are beginning to come through. As I move towards retirement it turns out I'm not in the blank generation at all, but am likely to become a silver-plated silver surfer.

With huge irony, these newly wealthy pensioners are the same generational cohorts putting massive pressure on adult social care and the NHS, and public finances generally.

Younger generations, which now stretch to Generations X, Y and Z (you wonder what next?) will see higher tax, lower public service levels, much worse private pension offerings and less chance of home ownership.

Within councils, the generational divide is also a feature. The traditional reward package includes automatic annual increments and a defined benefit pension scheme – we reward long service rather than performance. Not surprising, then, that many councils have a relatively aged workforce.

Electorally, older generations are both more numerous and more likely to vote, and so receive protections like the triple lock, winter fuel allowance and exemption from council tax support reforms, because their votes count for more.

The last election saw a resurgence of young people going to the polls, and a renewed interest in politics. Perhaps this is the start of a challenge to the generational divide that - a issue that policy makers centrally and locally must surely face up to. The brunt of austerity cannot be focused on younger, working generations.

I resented being in the blank generation. Now I don't want to be in the drain generation.

https://youtu.be/ozrWb_jRRHE

IMAGINATION (BEING THE FUTURE AND REALISING CHANGE)

"The desire to transform our borough is massively motivational."

Tom Hook, Barking and Dagenham

"Imagination is more important than knowledge. Knowledge is limited. Imagination encircles the world."

Einstein

CHAPTER 5

We are creating a new system, adapting and shape-shifting as we go. We can imagine how our sector could be different and are already being different. We make change through experiences, draw from different perspectives; we're quicker, lighter and move into interesting spaces.

IT DOESN'T FEEL LIKE LOCAL GOVERNMENT

TOM HOOK

There's a definite buzz in Barking and Dagenham. We're not about managing decline and our vision for the place is exciting, challenging and bold. It's based on growth in the borough, and our place in London, as a means of improving life chances, but also generating income long-term; we're driving it at pace and we've on course to deliver it.

Doing things differently is part of everyday life here and we are constantly trying new angles on things. It requires a kind of bravery and we have conversations that are both truly excruciating and genuinely brilliant. There's no time for back-covering or face-saving behaviours, we all expect to be called out on what isn't working. You need to be emotionally resilient and not take things personally. The desire to transform the borough is massively motivational.

We're one of the most deprived places in the UK with catastrophically poor outcomes for too many of our residents but also huge opportunities. Our mission is to help seize those prospects for the benefit of everyone. This has meant designing and implementing a new kind of council and forging a new relationship with citizens.

Accountability for delivery and changing outcomes is key to our model going forward, but we need to be sure that we understand what we're measuring, where we're starting from and where it's realistic to be in five, ten and 20 years. Our new insight hub is key to that realisation. What we do agree on is that it's all about the outcome and how we get tangible results for our communities.

As a service we try to work into as many interesting spaces as possible, to hear as many different views as we can. We made a connection with a local tech entrepreneur who drops into our management team now and again on a voluntary basis. It all adds new perspectives. But so do the 6,000 residents we've listened to in the past 12 months.

READING THE FUTURE

FICTION

I took a voluntary redundancy package after working for the council for 37 years. I never thought I'd want to leave; I am a public services professional right through the middle, but I couldn't carry on – every year got harder, cuts dominated, and we lost that sense that we were doing something worthwhile. The fun had gone out of it.

It wasn't just about work. When I was younger local government seemed more alive, local elections seemed to matter, and people felt passionately about what they wanted to achieve – articulated positively, not just as fighting austerity.

I found myself "retired" at 57, with lots still to offer, and that public service ethos still ticking.

At a loose end, I got involved in a community group that has taken over the running of our local library – the council closed it because it can no longer fund it. The irony of this is not lost on me – one council saving (me) working for free to mitigate the impact of another.

Truth is, I love it - I have a renewed sense that I am making a difference. The threat of closure has galvanised the community into valuing the library – they had always taken it for granted. There is a great atmosphere, and I have made some new friends, including my young neighbour Hitesh, who had never been in the library before. The range of activities and opening hours have expanded as local groups use the facility more extensively than they used to. The small of espresso now wafts away the smell of slightly musty books, the place is buzzing.

All this has got me thinking. If we set up a parish council, I reckon people would agree to pay more council tax to help the library – and I think that the process of asking the community might even rekindle the democratic process – give participating and voting a reality that's lost in the national system. Hitesh is certainly fired up by the prospect – it may also give him a chance for a job.

The community's got its library back, and I've got my mojo back. There's no need to stop here - there's a raft of things people want that the council can't provide any more, but we can. And there's no referendum limit to stop us...

LEISURE REINVENTED, RELATIONSHIPS CEMENTED... HEALTH ISSUES PREVENTED

RICHARD KAY

Can you stand on one foot with a pint of beer on your head? That's what we call pub yoga. There's also Paddy Power Ping Pong - table tennis outside the bookies. We are targeting physically inactive adults as well as people at risk of type 2 diabetes. Our way of doing that is to make a basic human connection, to start the conversation; talk to people wherever they are. And we're constantly reinventing ourselves, keeping it fresh.

To support people with mild dementia, we got a social enterprise to train staff in our leisure centres to deliver regular activity sessions. We sit down and talk to people, often with a cup of tea, to work out what people with memory issues and their carers need and to help them say yes. The conversion rates are great and it's really motivating for staff and for me. At a CCG management meeting I was able to tell them about real people's progress, like Olive who'd started with chair-based fitness and had recently got on a bus for the first time in years. I get my energy from work like this. I manage contracts and I'm always looking for ways to stretch them, find space to do work that gets results. It's nudge theory in action and it works.

But I find it hard to shout about the good stuff. Spending taxpayers' money engaging people through pub yoga at the same time as making cuts is a hard sell. The relationship between the council and local people is fragile. It's complicated by a British modesty and a lack of time I suppose. And maybe we're guilty of listening too hard to the loudest voices, the complainers?

I never shy away from a conversation and I never sugar the pill if things aren't right. The connection is everything. As leaders in local government we need to engage with and influence the whole system. We have to talk to real people and make sure our managers and staff do too. I encourage people to see the impact long-term of what we're doing and to get stuck in. Come to one of our sessions, experience it for yourself, then tell others about it. That's the way we change perceptions.

SEEING THINGS DIFFERENTLY

CLAIRE TOMLINSON

One authority I was supporting had a strong and well-regarded finance function but wanted, in their words, to "work together as one market leading team who puts customers at the heart of everything we do," and, at the same time, take a decent chunk out of their own budget.

If the service was to avoid being outsourced they had to move away from a back office function that produced reports, recorded, monitored and operated with silos. The council needed all staff to see their role as being at the heart of change and improvement and become business advisers who were genuinely interested in what the organisation wanted to achieve. It meant seeing things differently and getting into culture and behaviours.

What made the difference was building plenty of space for reflection into the process. Engagement can be time consuming but it's absolutely critical that people get time to think deal with the aspects of human nature that put the brakes on change. I believe you can't really moan about something unless you are prepared to do something about it. My mum said even as a baby I was very determined.

I have a strong public service ethos. I take hope from a wider group of people, who like me, work outside the sector but recognise and support public service. There's more awareness that we are all connected, even if you are a low service user. That said, when a member of my triathlon club was complaining about the council charging 20p to use the toilets, I pointed out that her bike cost a thousand pounds and that the small cost for her would support desperately needed services. If she didn't like it, she should get involved.

When we went back to see how the finance team were getting on, they were holding pop-up meetings to discuss topical or important issues. One finance manager said they had more confidence to challenge their colleagues to identify new ways of doing things, and another said that people were more open minded and contributed new ideas and perspectives in meetings.

One person said, "The small changes are starting to add up to something that feels quite different," – like the marginal gains approach British Cycling used to make incremental changes that were converted into all those gold medals at the Olympics.

For me, market leading isn't about an all singing, all dancing approach. It's about being able to change and adapt and continue to do the right thing at the right time.

KEEP FLITTING

MIRIAM LOXHAM

On day two in local government I accidently used the director's Norwich City FC mug for my cup of coffee. Now, approaching day 1,460, I always ask about the tea/coffee/milk/mug protocol when working in new teams. In four years there have been a lot of new teams – I've worked in arts and heritage, corporate assets and facilities management, parking, mental health services, housing and workforce development.

My latest role – a 12 month secondment – has involved moving to a new office. In my first few weeks while in the early morning queue for water from the eco hot water tap I saw a colleague who'd supported me with some work in my previous role. They wanted to know why I'd moved on. I fell back on my usual response.

"A new challenge, a change, it felt like the right time and it looked interesting…"

"But surely you've not been in your previous role that long?"
"True."

As the conversation progressed the term *flitter* featured. A flitter…someone who moves from role to role without ever really serving their time in the traditional local government way.

Clutching my mug of lukewarm coffee I retreated to my desk worrying about my flitting tendencies. It wasn't the first time this had pointed out to me. But applying a negative connation to it didn't resonate with me. I'd enjoyed it, I'd expanded my network of colleagues, made new friends, opened my eyes to the overwhelming diversity of local government work. I'd learnt about parking regulations, asbestos management and managing big bike races. I'd recognised difference and similarities, successes and failures, good management and less good management and at every step I learnt something that I then took away with me to my next role.

The dictionary definition of flit is *to fly or move quickly or lightly* and I've decided we need to make the case for more flitters in local government. People remain local government's most valuable and, typically, expensive asset. Austerity provokes new challenges and opportunities for how we use that asset.

Perhaps flitting is the answer? A workforce that moves quickly and lightly, ready to take on the next challenge and be deployed flexibly and quickly where required. I'm fortunate to work in an organisation that has given me the opportunity to flit, I like to think it's been mutually beneficial and I'm sure it's only a matter of time before I see flitter feature on a person specification.

CREATING A GLIDE PATH AND MOVING DIGITALLY FORWARD

GURMINDER SINGH

As consumers we use technology in our private lives all the time, interacting with businesses digitally, purchasing and banking online and some of us use Alexa which helps us make shopping lists. If local government was to use new apps, such as Alexa, to modernise and support business processes, identifying and making the top 10 customer contact points seamless, we could remove 80% of contact demand, improve customer satisfaction and staff morale in getting things right first time.

There are other examples that could make customer lives easier; apps that allows layering of all sorts of information using Google maps, all in real time – it could help services across the council in a variety of ways – but who is reviewing this opportunity? It's too easy to focus on re-procuring the same.

We need to build bridges that are comfortable for colleagues to walk across, that's the way we break through the silos and organisational boundaries. We have to break the cycle where IT and the other parts of an organisation disconnect.

So much IT change feels like it's being done to the organisation, not with. At Central Bedfordshire

Council we've spent a lot of time genuinely engaging with staff and understanding there's a generational problem we have to think through; almost half of our workforce are over 50. Leaders need to act like air traffic controllers; when introducing change in systems or processes we need to make sure there's a clear glide path and that movements on the airfield are viewed and managed so the volume of change doesn't bring the airport to a grinding halt!

It's important to take time to stand back and look at it from the outside and get feedback. Using internal colleagues upskills people builds succession planning and encourages internal movement.

Digital is as digital does. It's a new word and one many misunderstand. Digital should enable connections. Whenever there's resistance to technology I try to find a story showing how going digital helps and enables society. An example of this is the new 'Be My Eyes' app. It brings blind and visually impaired people together with sighted volunteers through a live video connection. I encourage people to try it out. I firmly believe in the quote which supports why digital is here to help everyone and in particular vulnerable and dependent people to lead independent and joyful lives. 'My humanity is bound up in yours, for we can only be human together.' – Desmond Tutu.

ABOUT SHARED PRESS

Shared Press is an independent publisher with a remit to share stories that engage with the sharp and messy boundaries of modern life; to give voice to new writers who care about ideas and innovation; and to inspire new creative conversations with readers.

We Know What We Are – *Dawn Reeves*

When a woman takes on the vested interests in politics and football, a city is forced to take sides.

A political thriller set in local government in the midlands, the novel explores shifting identities and allegiances and how principles are tested. *(Published October 2017)*

Walk Tall – Being a 21st Century Public Servant

Walk Tall is an inspiring book that celebrates public service and shows the way ahead. Featuring 65 public servants from 25 organisations, the book is an intriguing mix of stories, fact and fiction about the real challenges faced by public servants in the UK. It shows how people are thinking and resolving difficult issues and sets out the characteristics that we need in future to deliver for communities everywhere. *(Published June 2016)*

Making Our Mark

The world of work is a place where we play out the stories of our lives, where we learn and grow, earn our living, contribute to the economy and realise hopes and dreams. This creative book, commissioned by the University of Greenwich, focuses on student stories and experiences and is an invaluable resource for the university. *(Published in 2015, Global edition published in 2016)*

Change the Ending

What can fiction offer the public sector? A new perspective? An alternative way of working? Inspiration for the future? In Change the Ending, an intriguing collection of 350-word stories, senior local government officers, accountants, people in public health, social workers and many others rise to the challenge. The results are amazing – imaginative, forward-thinking, often celebratory, always stimulation. These are stories that matter. *(Published in 2014)*

Hard Change – *Dawn Reeves*

The novel centres on the compelling ramifications of a murder of a young girl. Neither a traditional thriller nor a conventional crime novel, it focuses on strategy rather than procedure and examines whether - and how – individual and collective action can make a difference.

For more details contact: **www.sharedpress.co.uk**